CGP makes SATs success non-fictional!

This brilliant CGP Stretch book is perfect for confident readers
who are ready to push their reading skills to the max.

It's packed with a huge range of non-fiction texts and extra-tricky
questions to help them aim for a top mark in the SATs.

There's also a useful scoresheet at the back, so it's easy to see
what they've mastered, and areas that still need perfecting.

What CGP is all about

Our sole aim here at CGP is to produce the highest quality books
— carefully written, immaculately presented and
dangerously close to being funny.

Then we work our socks off to get them out to you
— at the cheapest possible prices.

Contents

Section 1 – Frozen Escapes

Section 2 – Loggerhead Sea Turtles

Section 3 – International Fireworks Contest

Section 4 – The Real Blackbeard

Published by CGP

Editors: Izzy Bowen, Rachel Craig-McFeely, Emma Crighton, Catherine Heygate, Sean Walsh

ISBN: 978 1 78294 835 3

Printed by Elanders Ltd, Newcastle upon Tyne.
Clipart from Corel®

Based on the classic CGP style created by Richard Parsons.

Frozen Escapes

This text is an article about some unusual hotels that are built entirely from ice and snow. The reporter tells you about how these hotels are built, as well as interviewing some people to get their views about ice hotels.

What to do

1) Open out the folding pages, and read the article *Frozen Escapes*.

2) Have a quick mental break — let yourself daydream about what you're having for tea tonight.

3) Time's up — read the text again, and then have a go at the questions on the pages that follow.

Turn the page. ➡

which keeps guests coming back year after year.

Kevin Vernet, a French student who visited his first ice hotel last year, was amazed by the unique environment he discovered there.

"Where else can you relax in a fairy-tale carriage carved entirely from ice, or sleep surrounded by a menagerie of frozen animals?" he points out. "And next year it'll be something new entirely!"

Essex-born Carrie Tollington, who has spent every Christmas for the last 20 years in an ice hotel, is quick to agree with Kevin's assessment.

"It's an experience like no other," she explains. "You don't even notice the temperature after a while — I'm usually far too busy to realise how cold it is!"

When it comes to keeping guests occupied, ice hotels have an undeniable advantage. Many offer visitors the opportunity to try out a host of winter pursuits, such as dog sledding, skiing or snowmobiling. Inevitably, lots of ice hotels are located very far north,

which also makes them perfect places to venture out at night and catch a glimpse of the elusive Northern Lights — a spectacular natural light show which consists of ghostly waves of coloured light dancing in darkened skies.

Of course, outdoor pursuits aren't everyone's cup of tea, and so some hotels also put on less adventurous activities for which guests don't have to leave the comfort of the indoors. For example, visitors often have the opportunity to attend ice sculpting workshops, where they can try their hand at creating their very own frozen works of art. What's more, there's often the welcome relief of a scorching indoor sauna or hot tub, where guests can steam or soak to their hearts' content.

Building an entire hotel from ice might seem like an odd concept at first, but don't let their apparent lack of comfort put you off. As it turns out, ice hotels can be a fantastic escape for anyone, whether you're seeking a unique adventure or a relaxing winter break. Just don't forget your coat!

Marvin Okoye is a freelance travel writer specialising in Swedish tourism.

Find him at tedstravel.co.uk or email m.okoye@azmail.co.uk

25th February

FROZEN ESCAPES

Novelty ice hotels continue to grow in popularity as intrepid tourists search for unusual and innovative holiday destinations.

Reporter Marvin Okoye investigates the trend.

Hotels come in all shapes and sizes, but most offer the same basic conveniences — warm rooms, comfortable beds and the promise of a good night's sleep. Some hotels, though, go the extra mile to give their guests an experience that's truly out of the ordinary: they build their rooms entirely from ice.

Ice, of course, is cold, wet and presumably rather uncomfortable to sleep on. It's also prone to disintegration when the sun makes an appearance or the temperature climbs above zero. However, as tourism expert Johanna Burgess explains, ice hotels are not as impractical as they might first seem. In fact, some of the apparent disadvantages of ice hotels are actually key to their popularity.

"The vast majority of ice hotels are transient structures, built during the winter then allowed to melt away to nothing when the summer sunshine arrives. For those fleeting months in between, guests can experience the thrilling novelty of a sub-zero stay — if they're brave enough!"

Courage appears to be a key requirement for those who stay at ice hotels, where room temperatures have to be kept at a chilly - 5°C. All visitors are advised to bring plenty of layers to wear, and thick sleeping bags, blankets and even animal furs are often provided.

Although ice hotels are increasingly popular across the world, they are necessarily limited to places that have

The article continues over the page.

Section 1 — Frozen Escapes

the right climate, such as Canada, Norway, Sweden and Romania.

In fact, the world's first ice hotel was built 125 miles north of the Arctic Circle, in the Swedish village of Jukkasjärvi on the River Torne. The hotel was built in 1989, and every winter since then people from across the world have gathered in Jukkasjärvi to create a new hotel, each more extraordinary than the one before.

The River Torne is a plentiful source of building materials for the Jukkasjärvi ice hotel, which is constructed from huge blocks of ice from the river, each of which weighs in at a whopping two tonnes. Like most ice hotels, the hotel in Jukkasjärvi also makes use of another natural construction material — 'snice', a snow-ice mixture that acts as a sort of glue.

You might think that all of this would make for a delicate structure, but that's not the case — with their thick walls and careful construction, ice hotels are as strong and reliable as any other building, provided the weather doesn't cause any unexpected upsets.

There's one challenge that looms large during the construction of an ice hotel. Rooms have to be built at top speed in order to make the most of the winter season and enable the hotels to welcome paying guests for as many weeks as possible. However, it's also important that the hotels are safe to stay in, so lots of careful thought has to go into their design and construction. This planning takes time — ice hotels must always tread the line between speed and safety.

On top of the work required to build the structures themselves, it's not unusual for ice hotels to be decorated with carvings and sculptures, which are the product of many hours spent carefully shaping and etching the frosty substance. In Jukkasjärvi, for example, hand-carved works of ice-art are scattered throughout the hotel — previous designs have ranged from frozen dragons and polar bears to a London Underground train carriage. Hundreds of artists apply every year to create these magical masterpieces, but the vast majority are rejected. The ever-changing creative workforce means that each reincarnation of the hotel is completely different, and it's this, in addition to its novelty factor,

Fact Retrieval Questions

To answer FACT RETRIEVAL questions, you need to read the text carefully, then dig out the bit of information that each question asks you to find. See how you get on with these.

1) Read the paragraph that begins **'Hotels come in all shapes and sizes...'**
Write down **two** things that most hotels offer.

....

....

2 marks

2) In which country was the first ice hotel built?

| Romania | (Sweden) | Norway | Canada |

Circle your answer.

1 mark

3) According to the text, what is **'snice'** made of?

a snow-ice mixture that acts as a sort of glue.

1 mark

4) Why do ice hotels need to be built quickly?

So they don't melt in summer.

1 mark

5) Read the paragraph that begins **'There's one challenge...'**
Write down **one** thing that can slow down the construction of an ice hotel.

planing

1 mark

Section 1 — Frozen Escapes

© CGP — not to be photocopied

Here's what you have to do:

In Year 6 you have to take some tests called the SATs.
This book will help you do well in the reading bit of the tests.

The reading paper will test you on eight different reading elements:

2a Word Meanings   **2c** Summarising   **2e** Predictions   **2g** Language

2b Fact Retrieval   **2d** Inferences   **2f** Structure   **2h** Comparisons

These elements are used to see how well you can understand texts.

To help you improve your reading skills, this book has separate question pages for each of the reading elements — so you always know which one you are practising.

This is a Reading Raptor — it can read and understand even the trickiest non-fiction texts.

Your aim is to become a Reading Raptor.

Work through the questions in the book. When you finish a section, add up your marks and write them in the scoresheet at the end of the book.

Then, put a tick in the box at the end of the topic to show how you got on.   →

 If you got a lot of questions wrong, put a tick in the circle on the left. Don't worry — every Reading Raptor has to start somewhere. Read the texts again carefully, then have another go.

If you're nearly there but you're still a bit wobbly on some questions, put a tick in the middle circle. Ask your teacher to help you work out the areas you need more practice on.

 If you felt really confident and got nearly all the answers right, tick the circle on the right.

Congratulations — you're a Reading Raptor!

6) According to the text, which of the following have been sculptures in ice hotels?
   Tick **two** boxes.

a London bus	☐	a fairy-tale carriage	☑
polar bears	☐	a sports car	☐
flags of the world	☐	a snowmobile	☑

_____
1 mark

7) Why doesn't Carrie Tollington notice that ice hotels are cold?

....
_____
1 mark

8) Read the paragraph that begins **'Of course, outdoor pursuits aren't...'**
   Give **two** indoor activities that visitors can do at ice hotels.

..... *ue culpcrting* .... *workshop and make frozen work*
..... *of art* ....
_____
2 marks

9) Draw lines to match up each name to the correct description.
   Use each description once.

Marvin Okoye   **is a magazine reporter**

Johanna Burgess   **is a student from France**

Kevin Vernet   **is an expert on the tourism industry**

_____
1 mark

Reading Raptors can find any fact they need from a text. Can you? Tick to show how you got on.

© CGP — not to be photocopied   *Section 1 — Frozen Escapes*

Inference Questions

2d

INFERENCE questions are designed to get your cogs whirring — to answer them, you need to think about things that aren't as obvious in the text. See how you find these questions.

1) Read the paragraph that begins **'Hotels come in all shapes and sizes...'**
   How does this paragraph suggest that the people who run ice hotels care about their guests?

   ....

   ....

   1 mark

2) Read from **'Hotels come in all shapes and sizes...'** to **'...key to their popularity.'**
   Why might ice hotels seem **'impractical'**? Give **one** reason.

   ....

   ......*show nothing what does outdoor pursues .... principles ..*.................

   to.o

   1 mark

3) How do you think Johanna Burgess feels about ice hotels?
   Give a reason for your answer.

   ......~~bad~~ *because it can break*..

   ....

   2 marks

4) Read the paragraph that begins **'On top of the work required...'**
   What evidence is there that only a small team of artists work on each ice hotel in Jukkasjärvi?

   ......*on carving and ~~statut~~ sculptures*......................................

   1 mark

Inference Questions

5) Why does Carrie Tollington enjoy staying in ice hotels? Give **one** reason.

....you forget of the temperature...

1 mark

6) Put a tick in the correct box to show whether each statement is a fact or an opinion.

	Fact	Opinion
Carrie Tollington is from Essex.	✓	
Staying in an ice hotel is a fun experience.		✓
You can try skiing at many ice hotels.	✓	
Outdoor winter pursuits are boring.	✓	

1 mark

7) Why might a **'sauna or hot tub'** be a **'welcome relief'** for someone staying in an ice hotel?

....So the can be keep warm...

...

1 mark

8) By the end of the article, how do you think the reporter feels about ice hotels? Refer to the text in your answer.

.......alright because it could be one in a life......

....time ....

...

2 marks

Reading Raptors are the kings and queens of inference questions. How did you get on with these ones?

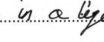

© CGP — not to be photocopied

Section 1 — Frozen Escapes

Word Meaning Questions

2a

WORD MEANING questions ask you about the meaning of particular words or phrases. Look at the rest of the sentence for help if you're not sure. Have a go at these questions.

1) **'For those fleeting months in between...'**

   What does the word **'fleeting'** mean in this sentence?

frozen	(exciting)	short	boring

   Circle your answer.

   _____
   1 mark

2) **'...ice hotels are as strong and reliable as any other building...'**

   What does the word **'reliable'** mean in this sentence?

   .... *better* ....

   _____
   1 mark

3) **'...was amazed by the unique environment he discovered there.'**

   What does the word **'unique'** tell you about the environment at the ice hotel?

   ....

   _____
   1 mark

4) **'Building an entire hotel from ice might seem like an odd concept...'**

   What does the word **'concept'** mean in this sentence? Tick **one** box.

   material ☐

   reason ☐

   idea ☑

   journey ☐

   _____
   1 mark

Reading Raptors love working out what tricky words mean. How did you find the questions on this page?

© CGP — not to be photocopied

Summary Questions

Read 'Frozen Escapes' again, then have a go at these SUMMARY questions. They're all about showing you understand the main ideas in particular sections of the text.

1) Read from **'In fact, the world's first ice hotel...'** to **'...tread the line between speed and safety.'**

   Tick the option which is the most suitable summary of this part of the text.

Crossing the River Torne	✓
The village of Jukkasjärvi	
Sleeping in ice hotels	
Constructing ice hotels	

   _____
   1 mark

2) Read from **'When it comes to keeping...'** to **'... their hearts' content.'**
   Write one sentence to summarise this part of the text.

   ....

   ....
   _____
   1 mark

Language Question

For LANGUAGE questions, you need to think about why the writer has chosen certain words, and what impressions those words create. Try out this question to test your skills.

1) The reporter describes the carvings and sculptures at the ice hotel as **'magical'**.
   What impressions does this give you of the carvings and sculptures?
   Give **two** things.

   ....

   ....
   _____
   2 marks

Reading Raptors are truly fantastic at summary and language questions. How about you? Tick a box.

Fact Retrieval Questions

2b

For these FACT RETRIEVAL questions, you'll need to hunt down bits of turtle trivia that are lurking in the depths of the text. Make sure you've read the text carefully before you start.

1) Read the paragraph that starts **'One of the most intriguing species...'**
Explain why loggerhead sea turtles have the name 'loggerhead'.

......to it large head...

_____
1 mark

2) How long can loggerhead sea turtles grow to?

............100 kg...

_____
1 mark

3) How often do loggerhead sea turtles have to return to the surface when they are **'active'**?

| (every few minutes) | whenever they need to eat | every ten hours | whenever they get tired |

Circle your answer.

_____
1 mark

4) Look at the paragraph starting **'Loggerheads are extremely well adapted...'**
a) Which of the following do young loggerhead sea turtles eat?

| eggs | sharks | large fish | (seaweed) |

Circle your answer.

_____
1 mark

b) Write down **one** thing that older loggerhead sea turtles eat.

......Crab and other shellfish...

_____
1 mark

Fact Retrieval Questions

2b

5) How long do loggerhead sea turtles usually take to hatch?

...... *60 days* ......

1 mark

6) What guides baby loggerhead sea turtles towards the sea after they hatch?

...... *The moonlight* ......

1 mark

7) Read the paragraph that starts **'Tragically, these extraordinary creatures...'**
Why might it be hard for a loggerhead sea turtle to lay eggs? Tick **two** boxes.

Human developments put them off leaving the sea. ☐

There aren't enough houses, so they feel unsafe. ☐

The darkness means they can't find the shore. ☐

Sea defences can destroy their nesting sites. ☑

Sea defences make it easier to leave the shore without laying eggs. ☐

1 mark

8) Read the paragraph that begins **'Even when loggerheads do manage...'**
Why can the sea be dangerous for loggerhead sea turtles? Give **three** reasons.

...... *The sea rise, cars and drains* ......

3 marks

Reading Raptors chomp through a few fact retrieval questions at every meal. How did you get on?

Section 2 — Loggerhead Sea Turtles

2d Inference Questions

INFERENCE questions are all about feelings and ideas that aren't immediately obvious from the text — so you'll really need to get your brain going in order to answer these questions.

1) Read the first paragraph of the text.

How can you tell that sea turtles have existed for a long time?

Give **one** example.

.... fall of the dinosaurs and the rise of humans. ....

1 mark

2) **'One of the most intriguing species of sea turtle is the loggerhead...'**

Is this a fact or an opinion?

.... Fact ....

1 mark

3) Read the paragraph that starts **'In addition, loggerheads are...'**

How can you tell that loggerhead sea turtles are strong swimmers?

.... they travel large part of the Earth ....

1 mark

4) What evidence is there in the text that female loggerhead sea turtles have good memories?

....

1 mark

5) Read the paragraph that begins **'When a female loggerhead reaches...'**

Find and copy a phrase which suggests it is difficult for baby loggerhead sea turtles to leave their eggs.

....

1 mark

| 2d | **Inference Questions** |

6) Read from **'When a female loggerhead reaches...'** to **'...the ocean's surface.'**
Why do the hatchlings try to reach the sea **'as quickly as they can'**? Tick **one** box.

to join their parents ☐   to avoid predators ☐

because it is far away ☑   because it is dark ☐

1 mark

7) Read the paragraph beginning **'These threats to the turtles' nesting sites...'**
How does this paragraph make the baby loggerheads' journey to the sea seem challenging? Give **two** ways.

....

....

2 marks

8) The text says that plastic bags look similar to jellyfish.
Why does this make them a **'particular danger'** to loggerhead sea turtles?

...the... can... get... stuck..

....

2 marks

9) Read the last paragraph. How does this paragraph make the reader feel about loggerhead sea turtles? Explain your answer.

....

....

....

2 marks

After a long day chasing chickens, Reading Raptors love answering inference questions. How about you?

2a

Word Meaning Questions

Understanding what words mean is pretty useful, which is why WORD MEANING questions are important. If you're unsure, use the text around the word to help you work it out.

1) **'Those which manage to evade these dangers can live almost as long as humans...'**

What does the word **'evade'** mean in this sentence?

| prevent | avoid | forget | welcome |

Circle your answer.

1 mark

2) **'They eat a varied diet of marine produce...'**

What does the word **'varied'** tell you about the loggerheads' diet?

...... *it is good* ......

1 mark

3) Look at the paragraph beginning **'As soon as they emerge...'**

Find and copy **one** word from this paragraph that suggests that the sea is safe for loggerhead hatchlings.

...... *tend* ......

1 mark

4) **'Tragically, these extraordinary creatures are now facing severe threats to their existence.'**

What does the word **'severe'** mean in this sentence?

....

1 mark

Reading Raptors are simply brilliant at word meaning questions. How did you get on with these questions?

The last few questions on <u>Loggerhead Sea Turtles</u> are under here. ▶

Loggerhead Sea Turtles

Since various species of sea turtle first began to cruise the Earth's oceans, they have borne witness to the fall of the dinosaurs and the rise of human civilisation. They are widely considered among the world's most majestic creatures, with streamlined bodies and powerful flippers that enable them to glide gracefully through the water.

One of the most intriguing species of sea turtle is the loggerhead, which gained its name due to its unusually large head. When fully grown, these creatures can be around a metre long and weigh more than 100 kg. Their size protects them from most predators, although sharks, killer whales and other large aquatic animals still present a risk. Those which manage to evade these dangers can live almost as long as humans, with some surviving for more than half a century.

Loggerheads are extremely well adapted to their maritime existence. Although they have to return to the surface for breath every few minutes when they are active, when resting or sleeping they can survive underwater for a seemingly impossible amount of time — even up to ten hours. They eat a varied diet of marine produce: in their early years they mainly consume tiny sea creatures and plants such as seaweed, while older loggerheads enjoy jellyfish, crabs and other shellfish. They are equipped with vice-like jaws, which are ideal for crushing prey.

The text continues over the page.

In addition, loggerheads are intrepid explorers. During their sea-faring lives they will map out large parts of the world, often travelling hundreds or even thousands of miles across the sea. Their swimming abilities are coupled with superb navigational skills. When a female loggerhead turtle is ready to lay her eggs, she will return to the exact same beach she herself hatched on, even though decades may have passed since she was last there.

When a female loggerhead reaches her ancestral beach, she will dig a deep pit in the sand and lay a large number of eggs in it, often over 100, before returning to the water. After approximately 60 days, the baby turtles, which are only around five centimetres in length, fight their way out of the eggs and up through the sand. At this stage they are highly vulnerable to predators, although hatching under the cover of darkness does offer them some protection.

As soon as they emerge, the hatchlings start the long crawl across the beach — their goal is to reach the shelter of the sea as quickly as they can. They are drawn instinctively towards the brightest light source, and so they tend to move in the direction of the moonlight reflected on the ocean's surface.

Tragically, these extraordinary creatures are now facing severe threats to their existence. For example, it has become a lot harder for female loggerheads to lay their eggs successfully. Human developments near the coast, such as roads, houses and car parks, can deter them from coming ashore, while sea defences, which protect coastal buildings from risks like flooding, make it more difficult for the turtles to get on and off beaches, and can destroy their nesting sites completely.

These threats to the turtles' nesting sites also have an impact on baby loggerheads. Light emitted from coastal roads and buildings can disorientate the hatchlings during their journey to the ocean, which may cause them to wander away from the sea. This leaves them at much greater risk from predators, and can lead them towards man-made hazards inland, such as cars, steps and drains.

Even when loggerheads do manage to reach the water, they are still in harm's way. One of the greatest dangers they face at sea is being caught in fishing nets, which can cause them serious injuries or even drown them. Ugly collisions with boats and propellers are also common. In addition, the pollution of the oceans with growing amounts of litter is a serious problem for loggerheads, who often mistake the debris for food.

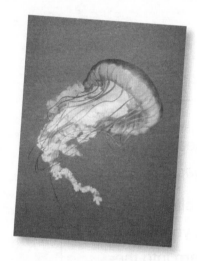

Unfortunately, a huge number of discarded plastic bags find their way into the world's oceans every year. Their resemblance to jellyfish means they are a particular danger to loggerhead sea turtles.

These problems may suggest that humans are always the villains in the loggerheads' story, but some individuals and organisations are now trying to protect these vulnerable creatures. In Florida, for example, people are trying to help loggerhead hatchlings by reducing the amount of artificial light emitted by beachfront properties. Other people have tried more direct methods to help turtle youngsters — on some beaches where loggerheads hatch, volunteers form human walls to deflect the tiny turtles away from buildings and roads, and direct them towards the sea. There are also many projects around the world which aim to clear up the cluttered seas and prevent more dangerous marine debris getting into them.

Conservationists hope that these efforts will be enough to secure the loggerheads' future. At present, however, the species remains in grave danger, and only time will tell whether these remarkable, ancient creatures will continue swimming through the world's oceans in years to come.

Loggerhead Sea Turtles

This text gives you lots of information about loggerhead sea turtles — a type of turtle found in oceans all over the world. In it, the writer takes you on a deep-sea journey into the lives of loggerheads, including the very first moments of their lives, what they eat, and where they travel...

What to do

1) Open out the folding pages, and read the non-fiction text *Loggerhead Sea Turtles*.

2) Give yourself a break — blink fifteen times in a row, as fast as you can, then see how long you can stare into the distance for without blinking.

3) Right, breaktime's over — it's time to move on to the questions.

Turn the page. ➡

Julie Rocquet, who helped organise the contest.

Not everyone has been so thrilled to see the return of the fireworks extravaganza, however. Sami Kalaji, chair of the town's Environment Society, tells us of his worries about litter: "Although we're proud that our town plays host to this dazzling event, it's a real shame to see our beautiful park flooded by a sea of rubbish, including carelessly discarded drinks cans and crisp packets."

Julie Rocquet assures us that the organisers of this year's event have addressed the Environment Society's concerns. Bins for litter and recycling have been distributed throughout the park, though some visitors have complained that they're not large enough, so they quickly overflow. The organisers have also drafted in a team of fifty gallant litter pickers to scour the park each evening, but despite these efforts, Sami Kalaji tells us that he remains concerned about the risks of long-term environmental damage to the park.

Anyone wishing to watch the displays should take note of official advice regarding entry and transport. With over two thousand people descending on Lakeview Park each evening, it's recommended that you arrive early to avoid long queues at the entrances. Parking near to the site is also limited, so attendees should walk or take public transport if possible. Guides will be stationed throughout the park to assist with any problems and ensure that everyone has an exhilarating and enjoyable evening.

Despite earlier warnings of high winds and heavy rain, the weather is now expected to be fair for the rest of the week. With opportunities to meet the teams on Wednesday and Thursday, and a special celebration on Sunday to mark the end of the contest, there's plenty of excitement on offer. Tonight, Bulgaria will be putting on their display — after a feeble performance last year, they are promising to bounce back this year with some novel techniques that have never been seen before.

← Open the flap for the start of the text.

International Fireworks Contest

You might have seen a fireworks display, but did you know that some towns also hold fireworks competitions? This article reports on the International Fireworks Contest, in which teams from around the world compete to put on the most impressive display.

What to do

1) Read the non-fiction text *International Fireworks Contest* — you'll need to turn over for some of it.

2) Then read it again — this will help you to be sure you've understood it all.

3) Now imagine it's the first day of the summer holidays — yippee! Have a quick daydream about all that lovely free time, then get on with the questions.

International Fireworks Contest

Skyline explodes with colour from around the world

The first night of the annual International Fireworks Contest took place last night, with thousands of people congregating in Loweton's Lakeview Park to witness the spectacle.

Each October, seven teams of fireworks professionals from across the globe battle it out in Loweton to be crowned the winner of the International Fireworks Contest. Every night during the first week of October, one of the competing teams showcases their pyrotechnic pizzazz in a twenty-minute-long fireworks display choreographed to music. There are also fairground rides to keep children entertained before the fireworks begin, and dancers and circus performers to round off each evening. Even better, spectators don't have to part with a single penny to get into the park.

The competing countries vary from year to year, although the USA, China and Ireland are all frequent contenders. The favourites in this year's competition are France, while the UK hasn't entered a

A shot from last night's display.

team this time around. Seeing how the teams will try to dazzle the judges is an exciting prospect — the competition is a chance for each nation to showcase their excellence in pyrotechnic creativity and innovation.

The article continues over the page.

This year's judges are a group of five international fireworks experts, ably assisted by two pupils from Loweton Primary School — the lucky winners of last year's 'Photograph a Firework' competition. After taking the very best shots of last year's displays, they'll be adept at using their artistic eye to determine the cream of the crop. The finest displays tend to combine a variety of different colours, sizes and sounds, all expertly synchronised to a compelling soundtrack. Some displays feature the latest pop music, while others are set to pieces of stirring classical music.

Kicking off this year's competition last night were returning champions, Canada. Despite a slight mishap at the start of the display, many onlookers have tipped it as the one to beat. Canada set off the largest number of fireworks ever used in a single display at the contest, and their show was set to live music from two of the world's most famous opera singers.

Fireworks over Loweton Lake.

Speaking after the display finished, 10-year-old Bethany Cawfield said: "I had to put my hands over my ears to protect them… but the colours were amazing — I couldn't believe what I was seeing! All the shapes were beautiful too — it was like magic."

Last night's crowd is already being estimated as a record turnout for the competition, no doubt partly thanks to the clear, dry weather. It was a great autumn evening for getting out and about, and ideal conditions for fireworks, with barely a breeze in the air. In the past, entrants have had to battle not only the fierce competition of the other teams, but also the terrible weather. Some displays have even been cancelled due to the poor conditions. Let's hope that this year's competition isn't marred by any such meteorological upsets.

The success of the first night has delighted the competition's organisers. Co-ordinator Julie Rocquet has spoken of her joy at the widespread enthusiasm for the contest: "It is especially satisfying to see so many people travel the length and breadth of the country for this event. For almost a decade now, the International Fireworks Contest has been one of the cornerstones of our community calendar." Local doctor Anna Riley agrees: "I've been every year since the contest began and these days I'm always one of the first to arrive at the park."

Summary Question

2c

SUMMARY questions ask you to think about the meaning of the whole text, or a big part of it, so it's a good idea to read 'Loggerhead Sea Turtles' again before doing this question.

1) Put these summaries of paragraphs in the order they appear in the text.
   The first one has been done for you.

   How and where baby loggerhead sea turtles hatch. ⬚

   A general introduction to sea turtles. ⬚ **1**

   How artificial light affects baby loggerhead sea turtles. ⬚

   The swimming and navigating skills of loggerheads. ⬚

   The issue of plastic bags in the sea. ⬚

   The breathing habits and diet of loggerhead sea turtles. ⬚

   _____
   1 mark

Prediction Question

2e

Time to round things off with a nice PREDICTION question. For this question, you need to use information in the text to work out what might happen in the future. Try it out.

1) Based on the text, do you think things will get better or worse for loggerhead
   sea turtles in the future? Explain your answer.

   better ⬚   worse ⬚

   ....

   ....

   ....

   ....
   _____
   3 marks

Reading Raptors summarise and predict faster than a speeding rocket. Tick a box to show how you did.

Fact Retrieval Questions

2b

Go fetch! FACT RETRIEVAL questions ask you to gather up facts from the text in the same way a dog fetches sticks. Well, a bit like that anyway. Try these...

1) How often does the fireworks contest happen?

....

1 mark

2) Which country is expected to win the competition?

| China | the UK | France | Bulgaria |

Circle your answer.

1 mark

3) Put a tick in the correct box to show whether each statement is true or false.

	True	False
Each team's display lasts thirty minutes.		
Spectators don't have to pay to watch the contest.		
The USA, China and Ireland regularly take part.		
A team from the UK is competing in this year's contest.		

1 mark

4) **'This year's judges are a group of five international fireworks experts...'**
   a) Who else is judging the fireworks contest?

....

1 mark

   b) Why were they chosen to be judges?

....

....

1 mark

Fact Retrieval Questions

5) Which types of music do the displays often feature? Give **two** types.

....

....

2 marks

6) Read the paragraph beginning **'The success of the...'**
What does Julie Rocquet find **'especially satisfying'**? Tick **one** box.

The record number of visitors to the contest. ☐

The excellent quality of the music. ☐

People coming from all over the country for the contest. ☐

The weather being perfect for a fireworks display. ☐

1 mark

7) Why have some visitors complained about the bins at the fireworks contest?

....

....

1 mark

8) **'Anyone wishing to watch the displays should take note of official advice...'**
What are visitors to the contest advised to do? Give **two** details.

....

....

....

2 marks

*Reading Raptors could win a fact retrieval competition
any day. How did you get on with the questions?*

Section 3 — International Fireworks Contest

Inference Questions

2d

INFERENCE questions need a bit of thinking about — they ask you to work things out using evidence in the text. Get your best thinking cap on and have a go at these...

1) Read the introduction.

How do you know that the fireworks contest is popular?

....

....

1 mark

2) Read the paragraph beginning **'Each October...'**

How can you tell from this paragraph that the fireworks contest is good for families?

....

1 mark

3) Put a tick in the correct box to show whether each statement is a fact or an opinion.

	Fact	Opinion
Fireworks displays should be very colourful.		
The music for the displays is always amazing.		
Canada performed first during this year's event.		
Canada won the competition last year.		

1 mark

4) Read the paragraph beginning **'Kicking off this year's competition...'**

How does this paragraph make Canada's display seem impressive?

....

....

....

2 marks

Inference Questions

5) Read the paragraph beginning 'Speaking after the display...'
What evidence is there that Canada's display was very loud?

....

....

_____
1 mark

6) How does Anna Riley feel about the contest? Use evidence from the text to explain your answer.

....

....

....

_____
2 marks

7) Read the paragraph beginning 'Not everyone has been...'
Find and copy a phrase that suggests a large amount of litter is left in the park.

....

_____
1 mark

8) Read the last paragraph.
How does this paragraph make the reader want to go to the fireworks contest?
Give **two** ways.

....

....

....

_____
2 marks

Reading Raptors can do inference questions while cartwheeling across the floor. How about you?

Section 3 — International Fireworks Contest

Word Meaning Questions

WORD MEANING questions test how good your knowledge of different words is. It's worth using the text around the words to help you understand them. Give these questions a go...

1) **'Seeing how the teams will try to dazzle the judges is an exciting prospect...'**
Circle the word that could replace **'dazzle'** in this sentence.

confuse	help	impress	disappoint

1 mark

2) **'...including carelessly discarded drinks cans and crisp packets.'**
What does the word **'discarded'** mean in this sentence?

....

1 mark

3) **'...the organisers of this year's event have addressed the Environment Society's concerns.'**
What does the phrase **'addressed the Environment Society's concerns'** mean in this sentence? Tick **one** box.

spoken to the Environment Society ☐

ignored the Environment Society's worries ☐

found solutions to the Environment Society's worries ☐

joined the Environment Society ☐

1 mark

4) Read the paragraph beginning **'Anyone wishing to watch...'**
Find and copy **one** word from this paragraph that means 'help'.

....

1 mark

Reading Raptors love word meanings more than they love lying on the beach in the sun. How about you?

The last few questions on <u>International Fireworks Contest</u> are under here. ➤

Scoresheet

Great work, you're all finished with this book. Use the answer book to find out how well you did and write your marks in the table below.

	Section 1 – Frozen Escapes	Section 2 – Loggerhead Sea Turtles	Section 3 – International Fireworks Contest	Section 4 – The Real Blackbeard	Total
2a Word Meanings	/ 4	/ 4	/ 4	/ 5	/ 17
2b Fact Retrieval	/ 11	/ 11	/ 11	/ 13	/ 46
2c Summarising	/ 2	/ 1	/ 2	/ 2	/ 7
2d Inferences	/ 10	/ 12	/ 11	/ 12	/ 45
2e Predictions		/ 3			/ 3
2f Structure				/ 1	/ 1
2g Language	/ 2				/ 2
2h Comparisons			/ 1		/ 1
Total	/ 29	/ 31	/ 29	/ 33	/ 122

Look at your total score to see how you're doing and where you need more practice:

0 – 55 — Don't worry if you got lots wrong. Revise the reading skills you're struggling with and then have another go at the questions.

56 – 100 — You're doing well. Look back at any reading elements you're struggling with and try the questions again to make sure you're happy with them.

101 – 122 — Good work, you're doing great. Give yourself a pat on the back.

Summary Questions

2c

Now is a good time to go back and read the text again — SUMMARY questions like the ones below are about the overall ideas of some or all of the text, so you'll need to know your stuff.

1) Put these summaries of paragraphs in the order they appear in the text. The first one has been done for you.

Details about Blackbeard's appearance. ☐

The discovery of a shipwreck and its contents. ☐

Blackbeard's life before he became a pirate. 1

The early years of Blackbeard's pirate career. ☐

Blackbeard's actions in Charleston Harbour. ☐

The events that led to the death of Blackbeard. ☐

1 mark

2) Circle the option that best summarises the whole text.

| the life and times of a pirate | comparing privateers and pirates | finding Blackbeard's ship | how to become a pirate |

1 mark

Structure Question

2f

STRUCTURE questions are designed to get you thinking about the text as a whole, including how different parts of it work together from beginning to end. Try this question out.

1) How does the last paragraph of the text link back to the first paragraph?

....

....

1 mark

Reading Raptors can never decide whether they love summary or structure questions more. How did you do?

Section 4 — The Real Blackbeard

Word Meaning Questions

WORD MEANING questions are fairly straightforward — all you need to do is work out what a word means in the text. Watch out for tricky words that try to trip you up, though.

1) Read the paragraph that begins '**However, after fighting for Britain...**'

   Find and copy a word from this paragraph that means the same as 'threatening'.

   ....

   _____
   1 mark

2) '**...Blackbeard gained a reputation as a brutal, violent pirate captain...**'

   What does the phrase '**gained a reputation as**' mean in this sentence?

   ....

   _____
   1 mark

3) '**One of Blackbeard's most notorious actions...**'

   What does the word '**notorious**' tell you about Blackbeard's blockade?

   | It was very expensive to do. | It's famous for being a bad thing. | Very few people know about it. | It was very difficult to do. |

   Circle your answer.

   _____
   1 mark

4) '**Blackbeard and his crew seized any ship attempting to enter or leave the port...**'

   What does the word '**seized**' mean in this sentence?

   ....

   _____
   1 mark

5) Read the paragraph that begins '**For a long time...**'

   Find and copy a word from this paragraph that means the same as 'curious'.

   ....

   _____
   1 mark

Ask any Reading Raptor you can find — they all love word meaning questions. How did you get on?

Inference Questions

2d

6) How did Blackbeard's **'sinister reputation'** help him as a pirate?

....

....

7) Read the paragraph that begins **'If the stories around Blackbeard's life...'**
   In this paragraph, Robert Maynard seems

| cowardly | desperate | clever | indecisive |

Circle your answer.

1 mark

8) Do you think the writer expects Blackbeard's treasure to be found?
   Explain your answer using information from the text.

....

....

1 mark

9) Do you think people were right to think that Blackbeard was so dangerous?
   Use evidence from the text to explain your answer.

....

....

....

2 marks

*Reading Raptors are head over claws for inference
questions. How did you find this page? Tick a box.*

Inference Questions

INFERENCE questions can be interesting — they give you a chance to think about the deeper meaning of a text. They can be tricky, though, so use these questions to help you practise.

1) **'...the most terrible of all was Captain Blackbeard...'**
   Is this a fact or an opinion?

   ....

   1 mark

2) Read the first paragraph. Find and copy a phrase which tells you that nobody
   knows for certain when Blackbeard was born.

   ....

   1 mark

3) Read the paragraph that begins **'Sailing along the coast...'**
   How do you think ordinary sailors would have felt about Blackbeard?
   Give a reason for your answer.

   ....

   ....

   2 marks

4) What evidence is there in the text that medicines were very valuable in
   Blackbeard's time?

   ....

   ....

   1 mark

5) Read the paragraph that begins **'One of Blackbeard's most notorious...'**
   How does this paragraph suggest that Blackbeard was honest?

   ....

   ....

   1 mark

Fact Retrieval Questions

2b

6) What happened to Blackbeard's flagship in June 1718?

....

.... `1 mark`

7) Read the paragraph that begins **'Fortune did not always favour...'**
   What was the **'agreement'** that Blackbeard made?

....

.... `2 marks`

8) Put a tick in the correct box to show whether each statement is true or false.

	True	False
Blackbeard worked for the British navy.		
Blackbeard's fleet had a crew of 40 men.		
Farm owners wanted to help Blackbeard.		
Blackbeard was killed in November 1718.		

`1 mark`

9) How did Lieutenant Maynard trick Blackbeard? Explain your answer fully.

....

....

....

.... `3 marks`

Reading Raptors think fact retrieval questions are tastier than crumble and custard. How about you?

Section 4 — The Real Blackbeard

as attacking ships, Blackbeard also targeted farms growing crops like tobacco or rice, much to the anger of their owners. Desperate, they turned to Alexander Spotswood, the governor of Virginia, who sent Lieutenant Robert Maynard from the British navy to chase him down. Blackbeard was eventually killed in an epic showdown with Maynard and his crew in November 1718. In a stroke of cunning, Maynard ordered many of his crew to hide below decks before the battle commenced. After the initial battle, Maynard's decks looked empty, and Blackbeard was left under the impression that the Lieutenant's men had all been killed. Blackbeard gleefully boarded Maynard's ship, only to be surprised in an ambush. Rumour has it that it took five shots and twenty slashes to bring him down. Maynard cut off Blackbeard's head and threw his body overboard — reports say that it swam around the boat several times before eventually sinking down into the depths.

For a long time, no trace of Blackbeard's life and his reign of terror could be found, but in 1996 the wreck of a ship — believed to be the Queen Anne's Revenge — was discovered on the sea floor off the coast of North Carolina. Since then, people have speculated excitedly that the wreck might shed light on the location of an enormous bounty that some believe Blackbeard stashed away before he died. A number of cannons, anchors and other objects have been recovered from the wreck by inquisitive divers searching for answers.

Unfortunately for treasure hunters, however, the rumours of Blackbeard's final hidden treasure have little basis in fact, and the findings from the shipwreck have done little to improve the situation. Nonetheless, any further artefacts brought to the surface from their watery resting place may well reveal new information about the extraordinary life and legend of the infamous Captain Blackbeard.

Open the flap for the start of the text.

The Real Blackbeard

This non-fiction text gives you a boatload of information about the pirate known as Blackbeard, who sailed the seas around 300 years ago. Since then, he's become one of the most famous pirates of all time.

What to do

1) Read the non-fiction text *The Real Blackbeard* — you'll need to turn over for some of it.

2) Then give the whole thing a second read, so that all the new information gets a proper chance to crawl inside your brain.

3) Take a minute to let it all settle in (and maybe grab yourself a nice biscuit while you're waiting). Then move on to the questions.

The Real Blackbeard

Although many of the pirates who once roamed the seas were undoubtedly fearsome, the most terrible of all was Captain Blackbeard, whose life has become a pirate legend. Blackbeard's name may make him sound like a fictional character, but he is thought to have been an actual person, whose real name was Edward Teach. Teach is believed to have been born in 1680 in Bristol, England. As a young man, he joined the British navy as a privateer — a sailor who had his own armed ship and attacked enemy vessels for his country.

However, after fighting for Britain for a few years, Teach, like many other privateers, turned to piracy. Initially, he joined the crew of the pirate Benjamin Hornigold, but in 1717 he captured a ship and became a pirate captain in his own right. Blackbeard named his ship the Queen Anne's Revenge and ensured that it was heavily armed with 40 guns. He soon added more vessels to his fleet, which was manned by a crew of over 200 men. With this menacing force, he took to attacking merchant ships and plundering their cargoes of food, wine, silk and weapons.

Sailing along the coast of America and around the Caribbean, Blackbeard gained a reputation as a brutal, violent pirate captain who showed no mercy in his pursuit of riches. The reputation of this piratical fiend was probably stoked by his appearance: he wore pistols strung across his body and had a thick black beard twisted into braids with black ribbons. Astonishingly, it is also said that

The text continues over the page. ➡

he would tie burning fuses to the ends of the braids, creating plumes of black smoke around his face and giving him the appearance of a demonic creature.

One of Blackbeard's most notorious actions was the blockade of Charleston Harbour. Blackbeard and his crew seized any ship attempting to enter or leave the port, and even took the passengers and crew of one ship prisoner. As a ransom for the hostages, Blackbeard demanded a chest of medicines. True to his word, when the medicines were delivered he released the prisoners, but not without first stealing their possessions and possibly even their clothes.

Despite Blackbeard's sinister reputation, the truth about his behaviour as a pirate is shrouded in mystery. There is no clear evidence that he was any more violent than other pirates at the time, and some historians believe that he never killed anyone. Instead, his frightful appearance and savage reputation enabled him to take over ships using terror alone — the mere sight of his flag approaching over the horizon was enough to leave many an honest sailor quaking in their boots.

Fortune did not always favour Blackbeard, however. In June 1718 his flagship, the Queen Anne's Revenge, was lost after it ran aground. Perhaps beginning to tire of his life outside the law, Blackbeard then sought a pardon, which would forgive him his crimes and enable him to establish a new life for himself. The pardon was granted, and once again, Blackbeard became a privateer. This meant that he could continue to plunder ships without fear of punishment, on the condition that he shared his spoils with the state governor — perhaps the perfect agreement.

If the stories around Blackbeard's life seem astonishing, those around his death are even more outlandish. As well

← Keep turning...

Summary Questions

For SUMMARY questions, you need to consider the overall meaning of a chunk of text, or even the whole text. Have a go at answering these summary questions...

1) Read from **'Each October...'** to **'...creativity and innovation.'**
   This section is mainly about

| the town called Loweton | how to put on a fireworks display | the fireworks contest in Loweton | the teams competing in the contest |

   Circle your answer.

   _____
   1 mark

2) Which of these is a main idea of the whole text? Tick **one** box.

   The International Fireworks Contest is famous. ☐

   Littering is often a problem at fireworks displays. ☐

   Fireworks displays are really exciting. ☐

   Music is important in fireworks contests. ☐

   _____
   1 mark

Comparison Question

Some COMPARISON questions will ask you to explain how something has changed in the text. Give this question a whirl, and see how you get on...

1) Look at the paragraph beginning **'Last night's crowd...'**
   How does the weather for this year's contest compare to the weather for previous contests?

   ....

   ....
   _____
   1 mark

Summary and comparison questions make Reading Raptors jump for joy. How do you feel about them?

2b **Fact Retrieval Questions**

The big challenge when answering FACT RETRIEVAL questions is digging up the treasure trove of facts that are buried in the text. Try these questions out.

1) What is Blackbeard's real name thought to have been?

| Benjamin Hornigold | Alexander Spotswood | Edward Teach | Robert Maynard |

Circle your answer.

1 mark

2) In what year did Blackbeard become a pirate captain?

....

1 mark

3) What was the name of Blackbeard's ship?

....

1 mark

4) Read the paragraph that begins **'However, after fighting for Britain...'**
Write down **two** things that Blackbeard's fleet stole from merchant ships.

....

....

2 marks

5) According to the text, where did Blackbeard sail? Tick **two** boxes.

the coast of Britain ☐   the Indian Ocean ☐

the Caribbean ☐   the coast of America ☐

the coast of Asia ☐   the coast of Europe ☐

1 mark